NEGROES
FOR MEDICINE

Report of a Macy Conference

NEGROES
FOR MEDICINE

Report of a Macy Conference

By Lee Cogan

Published for
The Josiah Macy, Jr. Foundation
by
The Johns Hopkins Press
Baltimore, Maryland

*The Negro people in this country
represent an emerging people with
every problem of an emerging people
everywhere or anywhere. In addition
to that, we are emerging in the most
highly developed country in the history
of the world. In addition to that,
we are emerging within a system where
there is a legacy of hate, a legacy
of distrust. There is ignorance and
there is lack of communication.
Negroes and whites have destructive,
defensive arrangements which have
been established over a long period
of time and are going to be extremely
difficult to overcome.*

Proceedings, page 321

*The biochemistry of sleep is wonderful,
because you get up every morning and
you see the sun and it is a new day.
You think it is possible to be happy,
no matter how much you have been scarred
up socially. But before noon every
day somebody reminds you that you are
an ebony man with a hoe.*

Proceedings, page 364

FOREWORD

Today the medical schools are joining the most intensive talent hunt ever launched in this country—the search for Negro students. Twenty years ago, only two medical schools in the seventeen southern states and the District of Columbia admitted Negro medical students: Howard in Washington and Meharry in Nashville, both Negro medical schools. Today all of the medical schools in the South, as well as other parts of the United States, admit and are seeking Negro students. But there are many problems—among them identification and recruitment in high school and college, guidance, preparation, admission, and financing.

This book considers the complex problems relating to preparing Negro students for the study of medicine and suggests some of the solutions to these problems. It is based primarily on a Macy Conference held in June, 1967, which was aimed at determining what can be done now to prepare and enroll more Negroes in the study of medicine. The participants included representatives of universities, colleges, medical schools, churches, the medical profession, philanthropy, and government. We felt that the discussions and proposals were of such significance that they deserved more than the usual conference report.

FOREWORD

We asked Mrs. Lee Cogan to take a fresh approach to a Macy Conference by preparing a book representing synthesis and provoking challenge and to discard the usual format of transactions with the identification of individuals in relation to their specific comments. We believe that Mrs. Cogan has accomplished these aims in a satisfactory manner. She has included many of the refreshing ideas that emerged from the discussions; in a sense, the forty-two participants whose names are listed at the end of the volume were collaborators in the preparation of this book. Although the problems admittedly are complex, there is an urgent need for solutions or for pilot programs that will point the way toward solutions. In the months that have passed since the conference on which this book is based, there have been significant developments to advance the opportunities for Negroes to study medicine. A number of medical schools have become "involved" in the problem based on understanding as well as commitment. Twice as many Negroes were accepted by the southern schools to enter the study of medicine in September, 1968, as were accepted in September, 1967. We hope that the book will stimulate a greater effort to prepare more Negroes for the study of medicine.

JOHN Z. BOWERS, M.D.
President, Josiah Macy, Jr. Foundation

PREFACE

"There is ignorance and there is lack of communication." These words, spoken by a Negro physician at the Macy Conference on Negroes for Medicine, accounted for and justified the calling of that conference. Mindful of the need for more physicians, and the need for more Negro physicians, the Macy Foundation, with the cooperation of National Medical Fellowships, Inc., gathered together from all parts of the country forty-two Negro and white representatives of the medical profession, of academic medicine, of government, of churches and of philanthropic organizations to break through the ignorance and lack of communication.

The conference was called to discuss and discover how to find more talented Negroes to come into medicine; how to prepare them, how to identify them, how to educate them, how to bring them to medical schools. The emphasis of the conference was on urgency; the goal was *now*: the next year, the next five years, at most the next ten years. And yet from the first words of the first speaker, it was clear that *now* was inseparable from *then*: that it would be necessary to look backward at what had and had not been accomplished and ahead to what could and could not be done, both short-range and long. It would also be necessary to examine the pressures and tensions, the conflicts, the contradictions, the ironies which had brought *then* to *now* and which would bring *now* to a new *then*, or perhaps a whole series of new *thens*.

The conference was a beginning. Much was learned and much was unlearned. This book, which turns to the light the many facets of the subject discussed at the conference and presents them for the consideration of many more people, is a continuation.

The book represents a distillation of the deliberations of the forty-two conference participants, often using the words of the participants and always reflecting their thinking. In the interest of readability and, in keeping with the spirit of the conference and the nature of the subject, comments, observations, opinions, and recommendations—all recorded in the transcript of the proceedings—have not here been attributed to individual participants. It has been my privilege to be the conveyor of their message.

L. C.

CONTENTS

NEGROES
FOR MEDICINE

Report of a Macy Conference

I

CONFLICTS AND TENSIONS

The position of the Negro in medicine is no different from the position of the Negro in America at the moment. The moment is one of contradiction, conflict, tension. The moment demands the truth, and the truth about the Negro in medicine today includes a number of contradictions, conflicts, and tensions.

The most severe conflict is that between quantity and quality. The entire subject of Negroes for medicine is permeated with this dilemma, as indeed is the larger issue of education for Negroes. The moment social reformers begin to speak about increasing the number of Negroes to be admitted to colleges, universities, and medical and other professional schools, educators are likely to respond with reluctant cries about maintaining high admission standards, standards of excellence

The Negro student, not brain-poor at birth, but privilege-poor, advantage-poor, opportunity-poor, frequently comes before the medical college admissions committee, if he comes at all, pitifully unprepared. Part of the Medical College Admission Test specifically measures verbal ability, but performance on the entire test, since it is a multiple-choice test, depends upon the student's verbal ability. His verbal ability in turn is greatly influenced by his home, by the quality of his early education, even by his opinion of himself. Can the

1

test, therefore, afford equality of opportunity? Can it yield a fair measure of potential quality? What is proven when culture-imprisoned people fail culture-bound tests? Test scores themselves can be variously—even subjectively—interpreted; arguments about the efficacy or inefficacy of the MCAT soon become merely an aspect of the quantity vs. quality dilemma. And if one argues that admissions policies must be relaxed, or that admission should be granted on the basis of applicants' potential for achievement, many medical schools answer that high academic standards must be maintained.

Negroes constitute 11.4 per cent of the nation's population, and yet only 2.2 per cent of the nation's physicians are Negroes. The need for more physicians is urgent. Medical schools claim that they are not discriminating against Negro students, that they are indeed searching for them. But are they searching for the good student, or are they concentrating on the so-called "instant Negro," the extraordinarily talented Negro student? If so, isn't this discriminatory? After all, not all physicians are equally talented. Why should Negro medical students have to be? Some argue that there is little purpose in raising the expectations of ill-prepared Negro medical students only to follow up with disillusionment and drop-out later on. But why, in order to be accepted, must the Negro student be better than the weakest white student admitted?

On the other hand, the recent emphasis on helping the underachiever, even the simple statement that not all practicing physicians or other professionals are equally talented, can lead to a dangerous assumption: that highly talented Negro students do not exist. The underachiever recently has received a great deal of publicity—justifiable publicity. But a plea must also be made, attention must be specifically drawn, to the Negro student who does have unusual potential talent. He must be sought out early, before he is lost to the profession (or to other professions) not so much for lack of special training but rather for lack of identification, guidance, and of financial support.

The arguments continue; the tensions tighten. There can be crash programs to ready another hundred, two hundred, even a thousand students to enter medical school at one level or another. Assuming that there are places or that places are reserved for these students, will the product of a crash premedical program be able to take the pressures of medical school? Can he meet the demands made upon him there, in addition to the pressures of his own past, the pressure of feeling called upon to represent his race, the pressure of standing out as a "loner"—as one of the few Negroes (or perhaps the only Negro) in his class? Is all of this really a service to him? There can be discrimination in both directions.

Despite these and other problems, crash programs do succeed. People react individually to pressure. Summer training and premedical training have improved the quality of many students. Questions arise from these facts. Should special training be arduous? Should it be permissive or highly structured? Should it concentrate on one subject or on several? How long should it last? One year? two? three? When should it begin and with whom?

Short-range crash programs which take a college student from a predominantly Negro school for a summer, or for his junior year, and then send him back, may never improve the school from which he comes. They may seem a blessing to the individual student, but are they shortchanging the Negro school and its other, less gifted, students? Surely short-range crash programs should not cause us to forget to help the schools themselves or to forget to help the Negro student long before he reaches college.

Nor do the problems end there. Is medical education, is the medical profession, too exacting in its demands? Too class conscious? Indeed, is the problem one of class rather than race? There are 2,000 colleges and universities in the

3

United States; 75 per cent of medical students come from 100 of them. In 1964–65, 195 Harvard graduates were accepted by medical schools in the United States; 171 of those entered.[1] At the Macy Conference, the estimate was made that not nearly as many as 200 or even 180 students from all Negro colleges combined were entering medical schools in 1967. Is this racial discrimination or is it class discrimination? Or neither? Is it the result of overly stringent demands?

Perhaps there should be a multiple-track system of medical education, so that a student who does not qualify for an M.D. degree might branch off into another of the health professions. Such a multiple-track system might also make it possible for a student who had been preparing for one of the health professions to go on for his M.D. if his performance (and his inclinations) indicate that he should do so. Unfortunately, the figures seem to show that students who fail to realize their ambitions to go into medicine do not go into the so-called paramedical professions. Is "track" education discriminatory, as has sometimes been charged? Or is it a way out of discrimination?

Predominantly Negro colleges and medical schools feel the conflict between quantity and quality, and many other conflicts. The dilemma, the contradictions, and the conflicts confronting these institutions as they fulfill their role in preparing Negroes for medicine also reflect the larger scene. The very term "predominantly Negro" sounds shocking at this moment in history. There should be no such thing. But if there were no prejudice, would it matter that there were predominantly Negro schools? And since there is prejudice, some Negroes may prefer to go to predominantly Negro colleges and medical schools, just as some members of minority religious groups prefer to go to denominational or "predominantly" religiously affiliated colleges and universities.

[1] *Datagrams*, February, 1967.

Naturally some Negroes prefer the absence of extraneous pressure, the relief from the need to prove themselves or to act as representatives of their race to the white world, which a Negro college or medical school can afford them. Some people feel, on reflection, that the Negro institution has a special place in the community as role model, as a source for desperately needed community health teams, and as a center of leadership. Others feel that there should be schools where Negro students who find themselves rejected by other colleges and medical schools can receive an education. The Negro woman who feels herself discriminated against either as a Negro or as a woman, or both, may find an opportunity for medical education in a predominantly Negro school. That segment of the Negro population which resents the white helping hand or the white middle-class exploitation of Negro anger should have the benefit of the symbolism of the Negro college and medical school as an alternative to anger.

But Negro colleges and medical schools, as a consequence of the very circumstances which brought them into being, are inferior institutions. They are underfinanced; they accept students with lower grades than do other colleges and medical schools; the ferment going on in science in American colleges has affected Negro colleges very little; they either do not have adequate physical facilities or cannot make full use of the ones they have. They cannot keep their best faculty members; Negroes as well as whites are unwilling to stay if they can command higher salaries elsewhere where facilities are better, and professional opportunities and challenges greater. Some of the superior Negro students do not want to attend these colleges and universities, a fact which further weakens them.

There are conflicting opinions about how to remedy this complex situation. Some feel that only vast sums of money can make any difference; others believe that there should be a start with endowed chairs, "centers of excellence," and that strength could then be added to strength. Still others

5

say that the poorest and weakest schools should be helped the most; and against that is the argument that only the strongest should be allowed to survive. Whichever position you take, the irony remains that good teachers are much more important now to Negroes than to whites throughout the educational process. As far as medical schools are concerned, the majority opinion (though there is a strongly felt minority opinion to the contrary) is that it is unthinkable to do away with any medical schools when the need for physicians is so great. The question is not whether there should be additional predominantly Negro medical schools, but rather what is to be the fate of existing ones.

The question of predominantly Negro schools is part of the conflict between the short-range and the longer, another pervasive problem. Perhaps the predominantly Negro medical school, which should surely be improved for the present and immediate (some say foreseeable) future, should ultimately become fully integrated racially. No one can predict when this will happen, which makes planning particularly difficult. For example, it is difficult to determine in this context, whether it is a service or a disservice to draw the better medical students away from Howard and Meharry. To the outsider it may all look hopelessly frustrating; but the administrators of these institutions, frustrated though they may be, are surely not without hope.

The answer or answers to the question "When is too late?" or "When is too early?" are different for the long range and for the short. To obtain the immediate objective of more Negro physicians *now*, baccalaureate or post-baccalaureate programs are not too late for some. For the long range, there is no time too early. Exposure of an infant one hour a day to a literate person can measurably affect that child's IQ. About fifty per cent of the children in predominantly Negro and Mexican-American or Puerto Rican grammar schools throughout the country, have greater than 50 per cent functional illiteracy.

Even here, differences appear. In rural areas, special educational programs for eleventh graders have met with considerable success pp. 27–8); but in urban areas, many students or youngsters who showed potential in the earlier grades have already dropped out or become unreachable by the eleventh grade.

Much must be done, both short range and long, to free the Negro from economic bondage. Medical education is the longest and most expensive of any professional training. Despite this, and despite the fact that most Negroes who do get to college terminate their education with the bachelor's degree, some Negroes do make it to medical school. Although some receive economic help from their families, others are obliged to send money home while they are at school. Many Negroes truncate their medical education, rather than go on to the specialties, for economic reasons. Many more never get that far.

Some economic help has been offered; much, much more will be needed, both from philanthropic organizations and from the government (another source of tension). But much will depend on respect for human dignity. It is a mistake to assume that people who need help want it and want it in whatever form it may be offered. It must be offered in a dignified way or it may not be accepted. When you try to help someone, you are in effect suggesting that he, or his background, is in some way inferior. Should financial help, therefore, be in the form of scholarships or loans or grants-in-aid? Scholarships are discriminatory (again the quality question); loans carry future obligations; grants-in-aid may be construed as derogatory.

One source of tension which all Negroes seem to agree upon is the visibility of the Negro, summed up in the epigram "You can't stop being Negro." (The implied antithesis is that you *can* stop being a member of any other minority group in America, which may or may not be true. But this, at least, seems to be a common feeling among Negroes, and

7

must therefore be taken into account.) It ushers in a crowd of social and psychological tensions and complexities.

It is important to remember that there are Negroes and Negroes. There are Northern Negroes and Southern Negroes. There are Negroes who are trapped in the rural South or in inner cities in the North; there are overprotected middle-class Negroes; there are lower-class Negroes overprepared for the professional opportunities open to them; there are lower-class Negroes unprepared for the opportunities that do exist. The attitudes of these different groups differ vastly from one another. It may be that attitudes toward them vary, too.

Sometimes the Negro medical student from the South seems to get along better in a Northern situation than the Negro medical student who was educated in integrated schools. There is, at any rate, social adjustment both ways: for the student who goes from Texas Southern to Harvard Medical School and for the one who goes from a predominantly white college to Howard or Meharry. It may be that the biggest contribution which a transition plan of supplementary education can make is in effecting the adjustment from one of these educational and social situations to another.

That attitudes affect performance need not be proven in this book. But there are subtle tensions here which demand consideration. The student who feels cheated by society may not work up to full capacity and may end by cheating himself, however unavoidably. On the other hand, a Negro student may fail because other people's aspirations for him are too high, because too many people are telling him, "We are all counting on you." The educational and aspirational levels of the parents of Negro students vary so greatly that the communication and incentive spectra of Negro students are extremely broad.

High school counselors, as well as parents, exert tremendous influence on students. High school counselors may be uninformed about opportunities for Negroes in medical school and in medicine; they may discourage students from

8

attending special programs, from applying to the best schools, from applying for financial aid, from taking the necessary academic subjects, or even from taking a chance. They may select Negro women instead of men for a variety of complex reasons which need airing.

There are discriminatory attitudes among academicians—surprisingly enough! They may be emancipated from prejudice intellectually but not emotionally. They may reward the boy who parts his hair the right way. They may talk down or answer down to a Negro college or medical student. They may assume that a Negro resident is not interested in or capable of doing research, and may steer him away from an academic career.

This stone also has another facet. Is the problem one of poor student-faculty relations and inadequate secondary school or college training and counseling—or is it the lack of confidence of the young Negro in himself and in his capabilities? Often the real problem is that competent Negro students have to face a sense of defeat, a sense of having been defeated by history and by the system, which makes them feel that they are merely going through the motions of a college education in order to get a secure, dead-end job in the post office. Or they may fail, though perfectly capable, because of fear or not being able to do the work. And then the high attrition rate is held against the next Negro applicant.

The attrition argument is a powerful weapon and another with many sides. It is used against Negroes; it is used against women; it can not as readily be used against Negro women as against white women, however, for Negro women are usually more likely than white women to continue working and to work full time. But any attempt to increase any group in which manpower is scarce will result in an increase in the attrition rate. Attrition is not a valid argument against attempting to enable more Negroes to go into medicine.

Even alienation or insecurity can be oversimplified, over-

9

generalized about. Experience is again individually interpreted; surely it cannot be classified by race. A first year
medical student would have to be psychotic not to feel in-
secure.

Much can be said about the "loner," the "symbolic Negro,"
the Negro who is the only member of his race (or one of a
very small number of Negroes) in a school class. Once again
individual differences will result in different interpretations
of experience. Commonly, however, Negro medical students
do report themselves to have felt excluded from the camara-
derie—the sharing of old examinations, study notes, bull sessions, social life in their medical schools. Although they report different thresholds of resistance to being hurt by such
experiences or to being able to handle the hurt they feel
it is probably not wise for the so-called "loner" to be literally
the only Negro in his college or medical school class.

The further along the Negro goes in medical preparation
and specialization, the greater the likelihood of social pressure. The Negro intern or resident, subjected to intense
pressures, may be tempted to shorten his residency or to drop
out short of Board certification. He knows that referrals and
hospital affiliation will be determined to a great extent by
social patterns and pressures. For these reasons, he probably
does not want to practice in a rural area, desperate though
he knows the need to be. And yet in an urban area, he will
also find himself faced with intellectually, emotionally, and
economically frustrating circumstances and alternatives.

Out of this tension, another arises, one related to the role
of the physician as a model. There is much talk about role
models, about how important it is for young Negroes to be
able to identify with members of their race who have become successful, influential, highly respected. By other
Negroes, the Negro physician was at one time the most
highly regarded Negro professional. But, largely because of
the conditions outlined above, the image of the Negro physi-

cian has dimmed among some Negroes and has been replaced by the image of the athlete. Part of the reason for this is economics. Part of it is exposure: the communications media have reinforced the fame of the athlete, have made him an "authority" on everything. The value of this to Negro youth is debatable. It may be unfortunate for the young man who will never be a good athlete but who is inspired by television to practice ball instead of studying.

The successful Negro professional, who could serve as a model, is faced with a gamut of choices. He may choose to dissociate himself from anything to do with race relations. At the other extreme, he may become a "professional Negro," who considers everything to be overtly or covertly tied to the Negro problem. In their struggle Negroes as a group need the involvement of successful Negroes. The successful Negro needs self-realization—the right to determine the extent of his own involvement, the right to fight for others the fight he has won himself.

History has willed the American Negro culture other stereotypes. The enforced matriarchy brought in its trail a number of stereotypical responses which are involved in the tangled subject of Negroes for medicine. In the Negro family, the girl, especially the oldest girl, is most protected and most often encouraged to go on with her education, out of practical awareness that it will in all probability fall upon her to support a family, or at any rate that more professional opportunity will be available to her. This encouragement further emasculates the Negro male, making it seem to him that if it is not "white" to study, it is "female." This set of responses is in turn responded to all along the way by members of the teaching profession. Nor is the Negro female left without psychic scar when she attempts to take her place in a white society in which intellectual prowess is associated with aggressiveness and maleness.

Many questions arise. Should the Negro male now be given preferential consideration (over the female) for medicine, to compensate for this skewness, especially since the future will no doubt see his social fulfillment? Can the Negro female—or any female—make a special contribution to medicine? Has the matriarchal Negro culture brought some benefits to Negroes—even to Negro men who have been encouraged and supported by their mothers? Should there be special educational and professional consideration for all women in medicine because of their dual role as physician and wife-mother? Should the woman physician, white or Negro, make it on her own, pull her own weight?

We have come full circle, or almost. No discussion of existing conflicts, contradictions, and tensions should omit or overlook the courage and endurance and faith that have become a part of Negro culture. The white man needs faith, too, faith and the sense of achievement which would come from participation in the realization of equality. Surely the black man's need for equality of opportunity is greater and more universal than the white man's need for a sense of achievement, but each man can learn from as well as give to another. Enlightened plans and suggestions for finding, training, and giving financial aid to more Negro medical students will obviously not solve all racial problems. But such plans and suggestions are needed by *all* men in this country, for all men.

No plans could be made without full realization of the problems existing at the moment, problems that we have aired here. Next we must review what has already been done to search out, encourage, and prepare Negroes for medicine. Only after that will we be in a position to make additional plans, both short-range and long-range, and to put them into action.

II

WHAT HAS BEEN DONE

The movement to improve the position of Negroes in medicine and the quality and availability of medicine for Negroes has had an extraordinarily short history; nonetheless that history bears examination. This summary is by no means exhaustive, but it is illustrative of the kinds of programs of supportive help that have been tried to date, in a struggle which has just begun.

Until recently, the Rockefeller Foundation was virtually the only philanthropic organization to do anything significant about the problems of health and Negro education in the South. In 1909, the Rockefeller Commission for the Eradication of Hookworm Disease was established. Its first director was Mr. Wickliffe Rose, a scholar of Greek from George Peabody College for Teachers at Nashville. The Commission, which soon became The Rockefeller Sanitary Commission, began its operations in North Carolina by attempting to distribute medication through general practitioners. It soon became evident that there would have to be a county-wide specialized organization for the program. The result was the Guilford County, North Carolina, health organization—the second in the country—and the gradual organization of county health departments. The need for specialized personnel to man these departments was also recognized. Out of this awareness came the development of the Schools of Public Health in this country and overseas.

Between 1916 and 1960, the Rockefeller Foundation, through its General Education Board, gave $8,673,706, exclusive of fellowships, to Meharry Medical College in Nashville, which was the sole medical and dental school which admitted only Negroes.[1] In 1960, the Foundation gave Meharry $400,000 to be used for a general drive to develop the college. Between 1926 and 1936 the Foundation also gave $587,000 to Howard University Medical School, after which the federal government began to finance it. The Foundation also established residencies and internships for Negroes at Sydenham Hospital in New York. In the summer of 1964, the Rockefeller Foundation, together with the Carnegie Corporation, sponsored five institutes for faculty members from predominantly Negro colleges in mathematics, biology, physics, English, and history. These institutes, held at Princeton, the Universities of North Carolina and Wisconsin, and elsewhere, attempted to bring these teachers in touch with contemporary science. To widen recruitment from the Negro high schools and to support Negroes in college, the Rockefeller Foundation gave grants to Emory, Tulane, Vanderbilt, and Duke in 1963 (for programs that began in September 1964). Presently there are 50 to 60 students under this program on each of the four campuses. The Foundation gave grants for similar programs which began in the fall of 1966 to Virginia Polytechnical Institute and Mercer University, Georgia, and for programs which began in the fall of 1967 to Cornell University, Bowdoin College, UCLA, and the Claremont Colleges. The grants to Cornell and Bowdoin strengthen already existing programs at these two institutions; Bowdoin plans to admit ten Negro students every year for an indefinite period. The UCLA and Claremont programs are chiefly for Mexican-Americans but includes Negroes as well.

[1] About 80 per cent of Meharry's student body is now Negro. (Flake, p. 11.)

14

The Rockefeller Foundation has also contributed to Fisk, Atlanta University, and Lincoln University: to Fisk to help pay faculty salaries and strengthen undergraduate departments in the social sciences and humanities and the business administration of the college; to Atlanta to create a cooperative effort among the four schools of which the university is composed; and to Lincoln to identify talented Negro men who might not otherwise attend college and to help finance their education at Lincoln and also to establish supportive pre-freshman and freshman programs there. When the Foundation grants money to the Negro colleges, it is not on a matching basis, as it is to predominantly white institutions. The Foundation has also given grants to small liberal arts colleges—Antioch, Carleton, Grinnell, Oberlin, Occidental, Reed, and Swarthmore—for these institutions to recruit Negro students and help support them through the undergraduate years.

Another early organization to give concern and support to Negro doctors, health manpower, and medical care was The Julius Rosenwald Fund, which developed health centers for Negroes in the twenties and thirties at Provident Hospital in Chicago and Flint-Goodridge Hospital in New Orleans. These hospitals were enormously important not only in improving the health of the Negro residents of the areas, but in providing facilities for one-year internships for Negro medical graduates, for whom it was so difficult to find approved hospitals where they could take their internships.

At the end of World War II, in response to local conditions, a group of Chicago physicians formed the Provident Medical Associates, built around Provident Hospital, for the improvement of medical practice through the financing of education and research. The organization soon became national in scope, interest, and support. Though not limited in its charter to assisting Negroes, the corporation did in fact so restrict its activities.

15

When the organization was founded in 1946, interest was centered on assisting Negro physicians to qualify for certification in the various specialties of medicine and surgery. This interest was originally implemented by awarding clinical fellowships for graduate study, and in recent years has been continued through loans, mainly to supplement the stipends paid to residents in training in hospitals. Since 1954 no clinical fellowships have been awarded to physicians in training for practice in the specialties, but loans have been made instead.

In 1952 the Board of Directors was expanded to represent Negro and white leaders in medical education nationally, and the name was changed to National Medical Fellowships, Inc. The organization became increasingly interested in the preparation of Negroes for medical education and in recruitment of Negroes for medicine. By June 1967, it had awarded $1,679,884 in grants to 538 people. Fifty people had grants from more than one category and 57 per cent received grants for more than one year—some for as many as four years.

To stimulate talented Negro college students to prepare for careers in medicine, the Alfred P. Sloan Foundation, in 1959, instituted substantial grants to National Medical Fellowships for four-year scholarships in medical school. The goal of the National Medical–Sloan Scholarships is to encourage students still in college or in high school to select medicine as a career, and to demonstrate that with proper selection Negroes in medical school perform as well as their white colleagues.

Other funds are also at the disposal of National Medical Fellowships. Grants-in-aid are awarded to needy medical school students who maintain acceptable though not outstanding records. Efforts at recruitment include various booklets which have been published through grants from The Commonwealth Fund, including the 1962 and 1965 editions of *New Opportunities for Negroes in Medicine,* of which over 30,000 copies were distributed free to colleges, high school counselors, and such organizations as NAACP and the Urban League. Workshops for premedical advisers have been held under a grant from the Sloan Foundation as another recruitment device.

For a time National Medical Fellowships administered a program in advanced fellowships financed by the National Foundation for Infantile Paralysis and the Commonwealth Fund for physicians who wanted to go into teaching and research in clinical medicine or into positions of leadership in community health programs. In 1960, when federal money for advanced study became available, these fellowships were discontinued. Predoctoral fellowships for college teachers in the premedical sciences financed by the National Foundation for Infantile Paralysis were also administered by NMF from 1953 to 1961. These fellowships were intended to encourage Negroes interested in teaching science to obtain the Ph.D. and thereby strengthen the teaching faculties of the Negro colleges.

One of the ways in which doctoral candidates and medical students have worked together to assist Negroes for medicine is illustrated by the Woodrow Wilson Teaching Internship program. The Wilson Foundation observed a restlessness among its Fellows attending graduate school. Some of them were bored and frustrated; they wanted the chance to teach. At the same time, there was a great need in many Negro colleges for young faculty. So the Foundation organized a program of teaching internships in the South in 1963. The program offered the opportunity to teach for a year to Wilson, Rhodes, National Science Foundation, and other prestige Fellows who had completed a minimum of two years of graduate work. The choice of interns was made by the individual college: the Woodrow Wilson Foundation paid one-fourth of the intern's salary. The participating college agreed that the Woodrow Wilson intern would devote one-fourth of his time working on his own with outstanding

Negro students. Some of the interns organized credit-carrying honors programs for this purpose. Often they were able to single out and recommend students for some of the more advanced programs of special training elsewhere in the country. Some Fellows stayed a second year; a few were sent on by the participating college to finish their Ph.D.'s if they did not already have them. While this program was not specifically aimed at enriching the Negro's opportunities to enter medicine, its indirect influence on this possibility is obvious.

Still another program of graduate fellowships is designed for teachers who commit themselves to teach for an undetermined time in predominantly Negro colleges in the South. This program, now being generously financed by the Danforth Foundation, is an outgrowth of the Southern Fellowship Fund, which has been in existence since 1954. However, this fellowship program has found itself at somewhat of a loss for volunteers.

Among other efforts to improve the quality of undergraduate education in the predominantly Negro colleges of the South—and again it should be emphasized that we are not making an exhaustive list, but merely an illustrative one —have been those of the Sloan Foundation. Several years ago, in conjunction with the Phelps-Stokes Fund, the Foundation established a counseling service to advise these colleges about fund-raising and development. In addition, the Foundation established a series of what it called "challenge grants" to upwards of 20 of these colleges, some public land-grant and some private, which would spur private contributions by matching grants, with special rewards for alumni and local contributions. About six months before the Macy Conference on Negroes for Medicine, the Sloan Foundation announced a $7.5 million dollar program of assistance to science programs in the liberal arts colleges. Twenty colleges were invited to participate, one of which was the predominantly Negro Morehouse College.

Under Title III of the Higher Education Act of 1965, federal aid is available to improve the academic quality of "developing institutions" of higher learning—colleges and junior colleges—which are "struggling for survival" and are "isolated from the main currents of academic life." These institutions may receive grants for cooperative agreements with other similar institutions, with the most advanced colleges and universities in the country, and with business and industry. Such cooperative effort may be for curricular or faculty development, faculty exchange, visiting scholars, cooperative education, the joint use of facilities, administrative or student-services improvement, or other similar efforts. Money is also available to these developing institutions on either a unilateral or cooperative basis for National Teaching Fellowships. These are one- or two-year full-time teaching appointments at a salary of $6,500 a year, plus $400 for each dependent. Their primary purpose is to encourage talented people to teach at the developing institutions, but they also free other full-time faculty members for additional preparation, strengthen existing academic programs or create new ones, and provide try-out periods which might lead to permanent teaching appointments.

These programs, and others like them, benefit the cause of Negroes for medicine by improving education for Negroes generally. However, existing programs have not done enough; many more are needed. The interdependence of the two is being emphasized.

Everywhere one turns in examining the problems of Negroes for medicine and medicine for Negroes, there is a spiral of frustration. Under-preparation leads to rejection. It also tends to perpetuate poor preparation among the next generation of students. Segregation results in—or carries as one of its concomitants—poor medical care. Competent, indeed first-rate, Negro physicians share with white physicians the reluctance to practice in rural areas, where medical care is most desperately needed. Even in urban areas, Negro physicians are frustrated; they have encountered serious problems in ob-

19

taining post-graduate and research training, and have been prevented from practicing first-rate medicine because they were chained to ill-equipped, understaffed Negro hospitals in which there were no formal educational facilities. Over-preparation—for the professional opportunities that may be offered—leads to frustration.

One current attempt to break this cycle is the establishment of the Charles Drew Hospital and Medical School in the Watts area of Los Angeles. Drew, named for a prominent Negro surgeon, is to be a county hospital with an interracial staff of uncompromising excellence, a postgraduate teaching hospital which will attempt to sustain intellectual ferment among its practicing physicians and to provide good training opportunities for interns, residents, and fellows. The hospital will be affiliated with the Charles Drew Post-Graduate Medical School, which is to be jointly sponsored by the UCLA Medical School, the USC Medical School, and the Charles Drew Medical Society. If the plan succeeds, the school and hospital will greatly improve the health facilities of the Watts area and stand as a symbol of brotherhood. It is another beginning.

The principal obstacles to having more Negro physicians are finances and lack of preparation among Negro students. Lack of motivation, poor faculty training, lack of awareness of opportunities, poor guidance, and hidden discrimination by medical schools in the form of the continued search for the talented Negro and the use of the culture-bound and therefore discriminatory Medical College Admission Test (MCAT) are others.

The Post-Baccalaureate Fellowship Program centered at Haverford College in Haverford, Pennsylvania, is one plan already in operation to do something immediate about the Negro who has been handicapped by lack of preparation through an inferior education and who now, at the point of graduation from college, finds that he cannot compete with other college graduates for admission to graduate or professional school. The plan attempts, to whatever extent it is possible, to repair in a summer plus a year the damage which has been done up to that point.

The Program had its origin in work which Haverford has done over the past half century with graduates of other Quaker colleges who needed supplemental study before going on to graduate programs in good universities or in first-rate professional schools. Originally, this extra year at Haverford ended in a second bachelor's degree; in the twenties and thirties Haverford awarded graduates of this program a master's degree. After World War II, the college offered other forms of assistance and discontinued the master's degree. Recently, building upon its previous experience, Haverford proposed the current program of post-baccalaureate work for disadvantaged college graduates who might wish to prepare themselves for advanced graduate or professional training but might otherwise be discouraged from going beyond the bachelor's, or at most the master's, degree. Initial support for the Program came to Haverford and Oberlin from the Rockefeller Foundation in 1965–66 and, that same year, in a small way, from the Woodrow Wilson Foundation, for students who intended to go into college teaching, and from the Smith, Kline and French Foundation. Then, in January 1966, the Rockefeller Foundation made a substantial three-year grant to Haverford to support a full-time director, special summer work, and 30 fellowships a year for each of the three years. In the summer of 1966 the Macy Foundation gave a grant to Haverford which not only contributed to the Program's ongoing expenses but enabled it to expand to include students interested in careers in medicine.

While the Program is not limited to Negroes, currently all of the premedical Fellows are Negroes. All students are required to take a summer program at Haverford—in a foreign language if they are planning to get a Ph.D., or in writing, mathematics, and molecular biology if they are going into

21

medicine. During the summer there is also time for personal discussion and assessment of career goals and for other supportive education. The students then spend a year at a strong liberal arts college—currently Bryn Mawr, Haverford, Knox, Oberlin, Pomona, Kalamazoo, or Swarthmore—filling in whatever gaps may exist in their education and preparing for graduate or professional school. These gaps usually include mathematics and organic chemistry. Haverford selects and helps counsel the students and is also instrumental in placing them later. However, they are under the jurisdiction of the schools they are attending and receive extra help and placement assistance from those schools.

Another intensive program which grew out of the need to identify and assist Negro and white students from Southern colleges who have potential for graduate work is the Harvard-Yale-Columbia Intensive Summer Studies Program. This program was initially financed for a trial year by a grant in the spring of 1966 from the Carnegie Corporation. Born of the questions and uncertainties of admissions officers about the qualifications of students from Negro colleges, the original plan was to bring promising students majoring in English or the social sciences in Southern Negro colleges to the campuses of Yale, Harvard, and Columbia during the critical summer between their junior and senior years for faculty evaluation and for faculty recommendation of those students found to be qualified. It was assumed that such students would be readily admitted to graduate schools, including the very best graduate schools, regardless of their performance on admissions tests, or their financial ability, if they could be identified. Further, the plan had as a long-range goal the strengthening of faculties in the Negro college, since it was also assumed that many of these students would return to teach in Southern colleges.

In 1966, 54 colleges participated. The presidents of each of these institutions appointed coordinators to identify nominees for the program and administer their admission. (Students may now apply directly to the Program for admission.) In addition to the more conventional application procedure, all candidates were interviewed at their home colleges about their special areas of interest. Students were selected on the basis of demonstrated capacity for rigorous creative work, interest in attending graduate school, financial inability to obtain similar training through other means, the capacity to benefit from a summer of intensive study, and finally the ability to help others benefit from the experience upon return to their own campuses.

The first year students studied such liberal arts subjects as English, philosophy, history, or sociology. They were enrolled in summer session courses and given special seminars and tutorials. At Harvard, they did work in the natural sciences. The curriculum was deliberately rigorous. It included a term paper which usually had to go through several drafts. Graduate students acted as tutors.

The first year's experience proved that a great deal of training was needed in basic verbal skills before students who were qualified for graduate and professional work could be identified. It therefore seemed desirable to take students between their sophomore and junior years to familiarize them with basic study skills and techniques and to introduce them to the concepts and methods used in their major fields of interest. Between their junior and senior years, the students participated again, making it possible to identify those capable of undertaking the rigorous sort of work that is demanded in graduate schools and to prepare them to meet those demands. In the second year of the program, the curriculum was expanded to include the natural sciences and mathematics.

The first group, who attended the Program in the summer of 1966, consisted of 108 students. Of these, 48 per cent continued their education beyond the baccalaureate in graduate or professional schools in 1967. Five of these students were enrolled in graduate or professional programs at Harvard,

Yale, or Columbia—according to the graduate admission officials of these three universities a substantial increase in the number of students admitted from these Southern Negro colleges in the past few years. Another ten per cent of the 108 were in post-baccalaureate programs in 1967 and were in the process of applying to graduate schools.[2] Eleven per cent had not received their bachelor's degrees but were continuing with their studies and planning to apply to graduate schools once they had their undergraduate degrees. In 1967, with the expansion of the Program to include a post-sophomore division, 65 Southern Negro schools participated; 200 students in the humanities, social sciences, and sciences —including five premedical students—took part. The Carnegie Corporation renewed its grant for the upper level students and the Ford Foundation supported the lower-level program. The statistics on the numbers of students who seemed, after their summer's training, to have graduate or professional school potential are most encouraging.[3]

Planned for the summer of 1968 were a post-baccalaureate program to give students who were in the post-junior program the opportunity to begin graduate work or to start work to meet their language requirements and a faculty audit program, offering 50 faculty members from the participating colleges the opportunity to audit graduate courses, participate in colloquia, do their own research, and discuss ways of establishing honors and other special programs for ISSP and other gifted students at their home campuses.

One of the indirect benefits of the Program was that it provided an increased awareness of the need for early counseling for college, graduate work, special work, military service, and careers.

[2] At the Macy Conference held in Atlanta in February, 1968, 51 per cent of the 108 were reported to be in graduate or professional schools. The figure of five at Harvard, Yale, or Columbia was unchanged.
[3] Harvard-Yale-Columbia Intensive Summer Studies Program Report.

Although the Program has built-in problems of its own, it also has scarcely tapped potentials.

There are, of course, efforts at recruitment to other professions which could serve as models for recruiting Negroes for medicine. One such model effort is the Harvard Law School Summer Program, which was set up in the fall of 1964 for the express purpose of encouraging Negro college students to consider careers in law. During the 1964–65 academic year, 40 students were selected for eight-week summer programs during which they attended law classes in the afternoon and devoted the mornings to an undergraduate course of their own choosing in the Harvard Summer School.

The law courses, modeled after first-year law-school courses but proceeding at a somewhat slower pace, are intended to give the students an introduction to law and an understanding of the work and responsibilities and opportunities of the lawyer.

Another pilot program in law which could serve as a model for medicine is the Emory Law School Program. Under this program, 12 students from Atlanta University were given a rigorous law-school course in torts during the summer. Nine of the 12 completed the course successfully and therefore were accepted at Emory Law School and given reduced programs for the first year. All nine completed that first year and continued on, forming a normal grade distribution from the top group to the bottom.

The Southern Regional Education Board is an interstate agency supported by the State governments of 15 Southeastern and Southwestern states, from Maryland to Texas including the border states of Oklahoma, Kentucky, and West Virginia, and southeastward from these states to Florida. The basic purpose of this organization is to serve as a planning and co-ordinating agency in the development of post-high school education. The organization has from the beginning had both research and education programs in higher education. The participating states agreed to pool their limited resources in certain graduate and professional disciplines. It was through this particular program that a relationship with Meharry was established. Each of the participating states contributes annually an amount based on the number of its residents eligible for financial aid. Interstate funds were also channeled to other institutions: Vanderbilt, Emory, Tulane, and some of the private predominantly white state-supported medical schools received students from other Southern states until those states developed their own public medical schools.

The same arrangement existed in dentistry, veterinary medicine, social work, and, for a short time, in public health.

In addition, the Board has helped state governments plan systems of public higher education. In 1966, with the help of a Carnegie Corporation grant, the Board turned its attention specifically to a program "devoted to encouraging and assisting Southern states in sound planning and action to provide equal opportunity to Negroes in higher education."[4] For carrying out this project, the Board appointed the Commission on Higher Educational Opportunity in the South.

The Commission set out first to "examine the status of the South's predominantly Negro colleges, suggesting the roles these institutions might play in the immediate and long-range future, and initiate programs to help prepare the institutions for these roles."[5] In its initial report, published in August 1967, the Commission commended the goal of providing equal educational opportunity for Negroes in the South and urged commitment to three general but necessary measures:

> 1. Immediate steps should be taken to help Negro college students overcome the handicaps of educational disadvantage and cultural deprivation.

[4] *The Negro and Higher Education in the South*, p. vi.
[5] Ibid.

2. Long-range plans should be devised to complete the evolution of the South's dual system of higher education into a single system serving all students.

3. All types of educational resources, including traditionally Negro colleges and universities, should be engaged in a massive effort to achieve equality of educational opportunity.[6]

Of special relevance here is the finding of the Commission that "Science teaching in the traditionally Negro colleges has been particularly weak, and a gigantic effort will be required to provide the resources—human and otherwise —which can boost it to standard levels."[7]

A beginning, a small beginning, has been made in tapping the talent pool of the unprepared—primarily lower class— students for higher education and professional training, medical training included. Here the thinking is to go back before college and search out those students who might never have gone to college at all, who are not taking advantage of available scholarship offerings, who are not working up to their own potential and give them special attention and preparation to enable them to become all that they are capable of becoming.

One such program is the Summer Study Skills Program which was begun by the Educational Counseling Service of the Board of National Missions of the United Presbyterian Church in 1961. The program began with 32 high school seniors and six hand-picked staff members. The students were Spanish Americans, American Indians, and Negroes from the southeastern United States. The idea was to give them six weeks of intensive, highly structured work in basic skills—reading, mathematics, English, and library usage— to help them do better on competitive tests. In 1964, eleventh graders were included in the program, which has had financial aid from the Rockefeller Foundation, the Southern Educational Foundation, the Doris Duke Founda-

6 Ibid., p. 1.
7 Ibid., p. 14.

tion, and the Educational Division of the United Laundry Workers Union. The students, who had had too little counseling and encouragement in the closed societies from which they came, learned new and disciplined study methods: how to budget time, plan, organize, schedule; how to approach a task; how to find information in the library and use it properly. They learned the great difference good teachers can make; they felt the effects of competition. The statistical results are inspiring: some students moved from the fiftieth to the ninetieth percentile in six weeks and stayed there; one, in mathematics, from the fifth to the ninetieth. There have been a relatively small number of students in the program; only a small but sharply increasing proportion were interested in premedical or medical courses. Many more students are being found and given this kind of intensive training.

The problem of getting more Negroes into medicine is obviously not separable from the problem of getting more Negroes into college. In 1963 representatives of twenty-one independent boarding schools convened to consider ways of helping promising students who are unable to make full use of their apparent ability because of lack of money or cultural advantages. It was felt that at least two years of an independent boarding school could assist materially in preparing such students for successful college entrance. As a result of that meeting, the Independent Schools Talent Search Program was started. It seeks out promising students from circumstances of disadvantage and places them in independent boarding schools under generous scholarship grants for the final two or three years of their high school education. The initial group of schools has expanded to over 75. Most students are from families whose total income is $4,000 a year or less. During the past four years, 850 students, 650 boys and 200 girls, have been sent to independent schools from all parts of the country. Another 150 were scheduled to enter in September 1968. Independent schools are generally not co-educational. Most of them are located in rural areas in the northeast—in New England, New York, New Jersey, and Pennsylvania—but there are a few schools in other parts of the country, including Arizona and California. The schools offer the most advantageous conditions for study: small classes, good library and other study facilities, availability of teachers, rich cultural and other extra-curricular programs.

As might have been anticipated, the students' transition from public schools to these private schools was difficult. To facilitate this leap, a second program was initiated for eight weeks in the summer at Dartmouth, Mount Holyoke, Carleton, Duke, and Williams called A Better Chance, or ABC. This program was designed to help disadvantaged ninth- and tenth-graders already selected by the Independent Schools Talent Search to make the transition from public to private schools. The students have intensive study in English, reading, and mathematics. They also learn how to use the library, how to study, and how to take examinations.

At the time of the June, 1967, Macy Conference, the director of the Independent Schools Talent Search Program was exploring with representatives of the Association of American Medical Colleges the possibility of the medical profession's becoming involved with the program in assisting Negro youngsters who are interested in careers in medicine.

The age level at which experimental plans for supportive education have been attempted and have proven successful varies, perhaps even geographically. In New York, for example, it was felt that youngsters who had reached the age of the eleventh-graders who responded so well to the Summer Study Skills Program would already have been lost to the schools or would be less pliable and responsive to help. One plan which is being tried in New York, the Provident Clinical Society Scholarship Project, begins with seventh graders and is working with them for a six-year period, providing a much-needed combination of firmness and enthusiastic concern. Three-quarters of these students are reportedly doing well, and are being aimed toward the top schools in the country, hopefully with the help of the National Scholarship Service Fund for Negro Students. The point should be emphasized, however, that the earlier any such plan is begun, the greater its chances of success. For students with the poorest work habits, from the more unstable family situations, even the seventh grade has proven to be too late.

The National Scholarship Service Fund is a talent referral system to which various colleges subscribe, including a large number in the group of 100 prestige colleges in the country. The service provides data sheets on Negro prospective applicants to college.

There is also the Cooperative Program for Educational Opportunities, located in New Haven, Connecticut. This was originally established for the Ivy League schools and the schools of the "Seven Sisters." But it has been expanded in the last few years to include a number of other universities. The representatives of these colleges interview Negro high school students who have applied or are applying to college. These interview reports are then reproduced and given to all the colleges in this cooperative venture. This greatly reduces recruitment activities and permits these schools to cover a much wider number of potential Negro students than would otherwise be possible.

Then there is the National Achievement Scholarship Program for Negroes, administered by the National Merit Scholarship Corporation, which not only identifies outstanding Negro applicants, but furnishes them with scholarship awards to attend colleges of their own choosing. It was reported at the conference, for example, that, according to the Director of Admissions at the University of Chicago, approximately 75 per cent of all Negro applicants come to the attention of the University via these three referral systems.[8]

Besides these and other referral systems, such as local recruitment by the colleges in high schools and junior colleges, there are the federally supported Upward Bound summer and academic year programs for ambitious, interested, and potentially able high school students. These are currently located at some 260 campuses in the United States. Some of these Upward Bound programs grew out of or were taken over from summer institutes for high school students at some of the predominantly Negro colleges. In the summer of 1967, 23,000 students participated in Upward Bound, in colleges from Pippa Passes in Kentucky to St. Thomas in the Virgin Islands. Sixty-seven per cent of students who were in Upward Bound as of May 1, 1967, matriculated in college in the fall of the same year.

In some areas of the South, a combination of the methods already discussed has been employed. For example, summer institutes for high school and college teachers have been combined with specially enriched one- and two-year college programs.

The Thirteen Colleges Project, an outgrowth of summer institutes, sponsored by the Carnegie Corporation, the Office of Education, the Office of Economic Opportunity, and the National Science Foundation, was begun in 1967.[9]

Faculty members teaching and counseling freshmen at the thirteen colleges spent an eight-week summer workshop revising freshman curricula and teaching methods, materials,

---

[8] The other 25 per cent, it was reported, are referred by students at the University, friends, alumni, and by local recruitment activities.

[9] The colleges are Alabama A. & M. College; Bennett College in Huntsboro, North Carolina; Bishop College in Dallas; Clark College in Atlanta; Florida A. & M. University in Tallahassee; Jackson State College in Jackson, Mississippi; Lincoln University, Lincoln, Pennsylvania; Norfolk State College, Norfolk, Virginia; North Carolina A. & T. University, Greensboro; Southern University, Baton Rouge, Louisiana; Talladega College, Talladega, Alabama; Tennessee A. & I. University in Nashville; and Voorhees College, Denmark, South Carolina.

and facilities—tailoring them to the specific needs of the students they would be teaching, getting away from conventional textbook methods and conventional ways of thinking in an effort to make learning more meaningful. The Project involved 1,250 of the colleges' total enrollment of 28,000—a total which is approximately one fifth of those enrolled in predominantly Negro colleges. In effect, it created colleges within colleges. The students were not necessarily preprofessional, but the implications are apparent.

The federal government, under the National Defense Education Act and the National Science Foundation, and the American Council on Education have also sponsored programs to enrich the backgrounds of teachers at the predominantly Negro schools.

In May and June of 1967 alone, the Educational Talent Search Program of the Office of Education, Department of Health, Education, and Welfare, awarded 55 contracts totaling $2,474,000 for the Educational Talent Search Program. Under this program, which is part of Title IV of the Higher Education Act of 1965, institutions of higher learning, state scholarship commissions, boards of education, and public or non-profit organizations are given funds to start talent searches to identify and counsel students on further educational training, publicize information on financial aid now available, and encourage both high school and college dropouts to resume their education.

Beginning in the 1966–67 academic year at Creighton University in Omaha, an experiment called Saturdays for Science took borderline C and low-B high school students into the medical research building for a few hours on six consecutive Saturdays. Faculty members in the School of Medicine lectured, demonstrated, and performed experiments in nuclear medicine, surgery, the brain and central nervous system, the digestive system, cardiac physiology, and nerve and muscle physiology. The students observed, learned, and were given the opportunity to question both the faculty members and themselves. Then these students were hired as laboratory assistants in the summer.

A similar project was begun at the University of Illinois Medical School in Chicago in 1965. In both places, Negro students have been encouraged to discover their potentials and to develop their interests, as well as to take advantage of scholarships which they had not known existed and which were going unused. In the 1967–68 school year, Omaha had over 100 students in its program. Also, medical students who are members of the Student Health Organization at the University of Chicago are serving as tutors in the premedical sciences to Negro high school students in an effort to encourage them toward the study of medicine. This project has now been assisted by a grant from the Macy Foundation.

The record shows that the problems of Negroes for medicine and medicine for Negroes are inseparable from the complex of social, psychological, geographic, historical, and economic problems surrounding the Negro. The Rockefeller Foundation began by trying to eradicate hookworm in a county in North Carolina and ended up financing a medical school in Tennessee. Begin with clinical fellowships and you might end up working with seventh graders, as in the case of the Provident group; with infants or their parents; or with the residue of insufficiency in Lumpkin, Georgia. Begin with six-week summer courses and you end up with four, eight, ten, or fourteen years of special education. Begin with money and you end up with people's feelings. Begin with trained doctors and you end up without adequate hospitals or hospital referrals for them. Begin with inadequately trained undergraduates and. . . . you are back again to the beginning, or before. Three hundred years ago. Three thousand years ago. On the Gold Coast, in Nigeria, in an underground moat.

Remedies in the future will have to be both long-range and short. There will have to be emergency measures even though they cannot solve the problem. There will have to be cautious measures and measures which may seem drastic. The future will have to model itself on the past and break away from that past at the same time. We will have to acknowledge what can be done and what cannot be done, and we can never be still until all that can be done has been done.

In the next chapter, we shall look at some of the short-range, immediate measures.

III

WHAT CAN BE DONE: SHORT RANGE

The participants in this Macy Conference came with an awareness, from their own experience, of existing conflicts and of past attempts—successes and failures—to alleviate the critical social and professional problems involving Negroes and medicine. They met with a sense of urgency to discover what could be done immediately to attract and assist Negroes interested in careers in medicine. Though the immediate future can no more be disentangled from the distant future than the present can be separated from the past, the 42 participants convened to recommend programs of immediate action, programs which could be put into motion within a year, or two years at the most.

The participants were asked to consider nine general questions:

1. Should there be a national scholarship program to identify, guide, and finance talented students interested in a career in medicine? At what educational level should the program begin?

2. Should there be additional predominantly Negro medical schools?

3. Is there a need for special programs to strengthen education in the premedical sciences—biology, chemistry, physics, and mathematics?

4. Should special programs be developed to attract larger numbers of Negro women for medicine?

5. What can the large, affluent universities do to assist in attracting more Negroes for medicine?

6. What programs can be developed to facilitate the transition of students from high school to college—and from college to medical school?

7. Should existing medical schools establish special programs for students?

8. Is there a special problem for the Negro student who is a "loner," or with only one or two other students?

9. Are there problems at the internship and residency level?[1]

These questions cannot be answered or even considered one by one. Some of them have been answered, if only by implication, in the preceding chapters. Some of them can be answered only by asking other questions. Some can be answered only after qualifying or modifying them. Some can be answered only by answering one or more of the others. Some seem to have obvious answers but do not. Some cannot be answered at all.

The proposals for immediate programs which grew out of the conference are themselves answers to some of the questions. Discussion of them was based on some hard facts about the present position of the Negro in education and medicine.

---

[1] For committee discussions, the questions were regrouped. Questions 1, 3, and 6 were discussed together under the title "Preparation for Medical Education," and proposals growing out of their discussion overlap. Proposals growing out of discussion of questions 5, 7, and 8, discussed as "Medical School Education—Selection and Admission," are also somewhat overlapping. Question 2, which pertains to another facet of medical school education, was modified in discussion to read: "What is the role of the predominantly Negro medical school?" Questions 4 and 9, together with discussion of the practicing Negro physician, were subsumed under the title "The Negro in Medicine."

Only six per cent of college-age Negroes attend college; more than half of these students go to predominantly Negro colleges. In these institutions the drop-out rate averages over 50 per cent. The high schools attended by these students often do not provide an academic or college-preparatory curriculum.[2] Well over half of all Negro college students are women, but less than ten per cent of Negro medical students are women.

A major problem facing the Negro candidate for medicine is poor preparation in quantitative reasoning. The greatest difference between Negro applicants and all applicants in performance on the MCAT is in the scores on Quantitative Ability. (This has led some educators to ask if too much emphasis has been placed on the MCAT in evaluating Negro applicants to medical schools.)

The weakness in science teaching at the traditionally Negro colleges reported by a number of observers, including recently the Commission on Higher Educational Opportunity in the South, has resulted in deficits in mathematics and the premedical sciences—biology, chemistry, and physics—which leave the Negro applicant severely handicapped in competition for medical school with students who have gone to better staffed and better equipped colleges, colleges which have consequently been able to keep abreast of changes in undergraduate curricula. When these deficits are combined with the Negro student's verbal infacility which is itself a result of both poor schooling and impoverished cultural surroundings, his handicap becomes virtually insurmountable.

Add grinding economic pressure to this picture and the result is that the need for a national program to strengthen Negro education can no longer be put in the form of a question. What does "grinding economic pressure" mean? It means 13 people living on $2,200 a year, in a house built on posts, a house measuring 20 feet by 30 feet, unpainted,

2 See Fichter, pp. 27, 29.

with cardboard walls, and a single light bulb. From a questionnaire distributed by the Institute for Higher Education to ten per cent of the students in 89 predominantly Negro colleges in 1963–64, it was estimated that over 40 per cent of the students' families had annual incomes below $4,000. A 1960 estimate, duplicated in 1964, reported only eight per cent of all college students' families in the country to be in that bracket. The same pair of studies showed 9.6 per cent of families of students in Negro colleges to be in the $10,000 a year and over bracket, contrasted with 41.1 per cent of families of all college students.[3] Another way of making the point is to record that, according to the 1966 Fort Lauderdale Conference on Medical Education, it was estimated that 60 per cent of all medical students come from families with annual incomes over $15,000, whereas, in 1965, only 15 per cent of all non-whites had annual incomes of over $7,000.[4] While estimates and sample surveys cannot be completely relied on, they cannot be dismissed either. The information gleaned from students at the traditionally Negro colleges seemed to check out against other college records. It is important to point out, in addition, that these students frequently have three or four siblings, so that the amount available toward higher education for any one of them is virtually meaningless.[5]

The rest follows inevitably. Many Negroes never get to college at all, regardless of their ability. Many more Negroes who do get to college owe money for college-incurred expenses when they graduate than whites.[6] A major reason why many Negro college graduates do not go on for professional and graduate training is lack of money.[7]

[3] Studies cited in McGrath, pp. 37–39.
[4] *The Crisis in Medical Services and Medical Education,* a report on an exploratory conference held February 20–25, 1966, Fort Lauderdale, Florida.
[5] McGrath, p. 39.
[6] See, for example, p. 59 of Fichter's sample study of the graduates of predominantly Negro colleges for the year 1964.
[7] Again, see Fichter, p. 60.

Financial help does exist, but "for the Negro in a segregated school in the South many of these opportunities are out of reach, either because of his background or because he is simply not informed and does not know where and how to apply for financial assistance."[8]

Two hundred Negroes graduate from medical school each year and the majority come from the predominantly Negro medical schools, Howard and Meharry. Under the program of the Southern Regional Education Board, Meharry reserves a majority of its first-year openings for students from the Southern and border states. However, with all of the Southern medical schools now prepared to accept Negro applicants on the same basis as white applicants, the willingness of state legislatures to continue to support this role for Meharry is doubtful. The number of Negroes applying for admission to medical schools throughout the country has failed to show a significant increase in the past two decades. Although the percentage increased from 16 per cent in 1947 to 31 per cent in 1955, the number decreased to 24 per cent in 1963.

Those Negroes who do make it through medical school are often forced by financial problems to enter private practice immediately after their internships; consequently only a small percentage of Negro graduates have been certified by the Specialty Boards.

These are a few of the facts.

With these facts in mind, as well as others which have been cited earlier in this book, the participants in the conference proposed programs that could and should be established now to prepare more Negroes for the study of medicine. The proposals are most compelling and warrant immediate attention.

[8] Reitzes, (1958) Introduction by McLean, p. xxiv.

There should be a national awards program for Negro students interested in the study of medicine, and it should begin at the end of the first year of college. The amount of the award should be based on need and the recipients should be assured that, if they prove themselves capable, support will be available throughout their medical education (or through medical school and in modified form through the post-graduate years).

We have admitted a serious need for more physicians in this country, and Negroes can provide an immediate increase both in numbers and in quality of our physicians. At present the Negro is being denied an equal opportunity to enjoy the privileges, responsibilities, and rewards of the medical profession. The foundations can help, as they are helping now, but foundations alone can never provide enough awards or enough support per award to meet the total need. It is manifestly impossible to identify students of any race at the undergraduate level, all of whom will continue and complete the study of medicine and become physicians. Surely, some can be identified at that time. Of course more could be identified accurately in the third year, but by then they would be in debt. They should therefore be able to qualify for such a program by the end of their first year. Of those who do not make it, many may well turn to health careers. The urgency with which manpower in these careers is also needed makes the demand for such a national awards program all the more compelling.

There was no disagreement among the participants at the conference on the question of a national scholarship program. There was considerable discussion of some of the refinements of the question. First in the word order of question one as it was posed is the word "scholarship" itself. In the first place, the term connotes excellence. As we said earlier, the idea of excellence gave rise to all but unanswerable questions. These questions are interesting and challenging, and should be taken into account by those who administer the proposed program; still, the program cannot and should not be delayed until all questions are answered. That not all members of any profession are equally talented should be kept in mind. The search should be for good people, some of whom will be greatly talented and some of whom will not be so talented. Many successful physicians are highly competent rather than extraordinarily talented. That the continued search for talent can become part of a pattern of bias and discrimination should be kept in mind. The argument is used that it isn't fair to accept a student for medical school unless there is assurance that he will succeed, and the corollary is that a Negro student must be a little better than the weakest white students admitted, in order to get a place. This whole argument seems discriminatory. A Negro does not have to be at the top of his class to be a good physician any more than a white student does. There can be only one at the top anyway. Responses to words are emotional, and it is important to remember that Negroes, along with all other people, will be hypersensitive to words which they construe as derogatory, as well as to help which implies condescension. The term "awards" was selected instead of "scholarship" or "traineeship" for this reason.

The feeling was almost unanimous that during the college years it should be an outright grant, whatever its title. The student should not be in debt for his education when he graduates from college. In medical school perhaps it should be three parts gift and one part loan, so arranged that the student would complete any residency he might undertake before being expected to repay the loan.

There should be a generous program for forgiveness of whatever debts there might be. For example, a doctor who practiced in a community where the ratio of physicians to population was low, or in the armed forces, might be forgiven a certain amount of his loan.

41

The program must identify and guide students interested in careers in medicine, not merely finance them. Identification is particularly difficult, but particularly important. The present inadequacy of high school and college premedical advisory programs acts as a major deterrent to attracting larger numbers of Negro students into medical careers.

There is an urgent need to inform high school and college guidance personnel and premedical advisers about the opportunities open to interested students. More communication among the high schools, colleges, and medical schools would help to solve many of the problems faced by students in transition from one level of education to another.

The medical schools themselves should take the lead here and make the facts known to key people in high schools and colleges. The availability of accurate, reliable information about openings, opportunities, and requirements would help students to decide (and Negro students seem to make career decisions at an earlier age than white students do) about careers in medicine and would help them to prepare more adequately for those careers.

There is urgent need for a program through which one or more faculty members at each of the predominantly Negro colleges could become informed about requirements for admission to medical school, the admissions process, the medical school curriculum, current attitudes toward the education of Negro students (for there may be considerable lag here between real and assumed attitudes), *and opportunities for Negro physicians.*

The information could be given to selected faculty members at Negro colleges through workshops developed by the medical schools and the Association of American Medical Colleges. The conferees suggested two ways in which advisory programs could be made more dynamic. The first was to foster premedical societies at the colleges, and the second was to improve communications between medical school admissions officers and the informed faculty people at the Negro colleges. Medical school admissions officers and premedical advisers might also visit high schools and colleges in which the existing advisory system is weak and speak with interested students. These visits might even include interviews with promising freshmen followed by assurance of places for them in specific medical schools if their school records warrant them.

The opportunities in medicine must be made known not only to the Negro who is a prospective college and medical student and to his school advisers, but also to his parents and to the various other adults who may counsel or influence him. The gigantic task of influencing several generations at once requires a multi-pronged campaign, reaching beyond the campus or high school into churches, community organizations, homes. It should make use of all existing media—radio; television; magazines; newspapers; and, always most important, word-of-mouth: talk-ins, meetings, conversations, especially involving Negro medical students or Negro physicians.

The question of the educational level at which a national program or programs should begin immediately gives rise to another question: How soon are we talking about? For the short range, the view with which this chapter is concerned, the college level was given priority by the conference participants. The national scholarship program, they felt, should begin as soon as possible and it should begin with the sophomore year of college. It is obviously important, long-range, to get down below the college level. But let us not write off the current college students. There are many Negro students in college now who, if their guidance and preparation were strengthened, could become qualified and definitely increase the number of Negroes in medical schools. They should be given financial support to provide economic assurance of their passage through medical school. This will not only achieve the immediate objective of enabling more Negroes to go to medical school, but will also demonstrate

43

success for students on Negro college campuses and thereby may serve to stimulate and motivate others to perform well enough to qualify. The tangles of motivation and career selection, of which the participants were all well aware, obviously could not be thoroughly dealt with at the conference. However, there was repeated reference to them—to role models, for example, and the part they play in career choices. Unfortunately (some participants, however, thought it fortunate) the image of the Negro physician, which used to occupy unchallenged first place in the Negro community as career choice, has been replaced by the image of the athlete. One reason given for this was the part played by the mass media. It is not quite that simple, however. The rewards for the Negro physician, financial, social, professional, have not lived up to expectation and this fact has made itself felt. Pumping in short-range motivation will not work unless, long-range, the rewards justify the motivation.

Career choices are not always made with the facts in mind; indeed, they are often made on the basis of inadequate information. Many people seem to have been influenced by a relative or their family physician or even by prolonged childhood illnesses which brought them into close and frequent contact with physicians and other people in health professions. Although it *is* true that one of the chief influences in career choice is another human being, it does not seem, as one might assume it would, that children of Negro physicians are especially likely to choose medicine as a career. Apparently the whole question of career choices is still muddy and deserves further study. It was suggested that money might well be allocated for that purpose.

Motivation, identification, guidance, financial aid—all are necessary for reaching the immediate goal. But motivating Negro college students to choose careers in medicine, and establishing traineeships to make the necessary expensive education available, is not enough if, in fact, these students are going to fail because they are not adequately prepared for the pace of medical school. We cannot stop at a national program, or a national program plus advice.

Northern medical schools are now eager to admit Negro students who are well enough prepared to compete successfully with the other highly selected students at these schools. Indeed, some of these medical schools have begun to ease their admission requirements for specific Negro students who, in the school's estimation, have the ability to compete successfully. Academic and cultural barriers have prevented these schools, however, from accepting and graduating more than a pitiful few. Some of the best medical schools in the country do not require that medical students be undergraduate science majors. They require a minimum of one full college course (one academic year) in physics, two in chemistry, one in biology, and mathematics through calculus. An important point is that although the names of these courses have not changed in the past ten years, their content has changed enormously in the better colleges. Take, for example, biology. Taxonomy, natural history, and evolution of plants and animals formerly filled much of the college biology courses. Now these have been moved back more and more into the high school courses, while the colleges have become increasingly concerned with molecular biology and biophysics. Ten years ago, when medical schools taught the electron microscopic structure of tissues, they were exposing students to material they had not had in college. Now medical school students from Princeton, Harvard, Columbia, and other such colleges are already familiar with this material from their undergraduate courses. They may not be very expert in using a light microscope, but in general they are already sophisticated in biological chemistry, molecular biology, microbial genetics, and the like.

It is obvious that many of the colleges to which the majority of Negro students go for economic and geographic and other reasons have not had the fiscal resources or faculty (often the same thing, but not always) to keep abreast of the rapid changes in emphasis and content of the sciences basic to medicine. The faculties of the Negro colleges must be helped and helped quickly, to prepare their students for medical education. As part of its plan of immediate action, the conference proposed that *there be a major effort to strengthen the teaching of the premedical sciences—and English—at the predominantly Negro colleges*. This could be begun by selecting a half-dozen colleges for financial support of faculty, purchase of equipment, and improvement of facilities by construction or remodeling.

Again, some disagreement centered around the question of excellence. There were those who thought that the schools which needed strengthening were not the ones which were already strong but the intermediate ones. The argument was that this would be the more fruitful way to increase the number of adequately prepared college graduates. However, opponents of this view felt that the way to build excellence is, as was cited earlier, to build strength on strength. The immediate future, this argument ran, is built upon the past. Most of the southern Negro medical students have been coming from five or six of the better predominantly Negro southern colleges. These, then, are the colleges to strengthen *first*. The longer-range objective is to improve the quality of the whole spectrum of colleges.

The relative weakness of even the best Negro colleges has been amply documented. Laboratory facilities and equipment are inadequate and out of date; libraries are poorly stocked; the science curriculum must be modernized; curricular options must be expanded to include more and better courses in the sciences (curricula in these colleges are heavily weighted toward the humanities); there are too few faculty members in the sciences, and those who are there are underpaid and relatively poorly trained: salaries must be raised if qualified faculty are to be recruited and enabled to take leaves of absence to continue their intellectual development and technical know-how.[9]

Summer workshops for faculty members at the predominantly Negro colleges such as those sponsored by the Rockefeller Foundation and the Esso Foundation, with help from the Office of Economic Opportunity and the Office of Education, should be encouraged and expanded.

Along with this supportive help for the colleges themselves, and for their faculties particularly, the importance of the teaching of English cannot be overstated. Discrimination against Negroes resulting from or hidden behind poor performance on admissions tests which require high verbal facility has already been discussed. Indeed, success on all written examinations requires verbal facility—not only in answering the questions but in understanding them. Subtler forms of social discrimination, with concomitant psychological pressures and effects upon performance, may also, however unconsciously, result from verbal infacility.

These problems do not begin at the college level. Long-range solutions reach back to the lower schools. But if we are to add to the number of Negroes accepted into medical school and to the number of Negro physicians in the next few years, we must emphasize the college level. And so workshops and specially devised curricula and curricular materials must be devised and expanded in the teaching of English as well as science and mathematics at the colleges.

Another step in assuring adequate premedical preparation of larger numbers of Negro students would be for the two predominantly Negro medical schools to establish special premedical programs—Howard with the liberal arts college of Howard University and Meharry with her neighbor, Fisk University. It was pointed out that medical schools in Britain, France, and Germany have long taught their own premedical sciences.

[9] See McGrath; Severinghaus *et al.*; and Commission on Higher Educational Opportunity in the South.

By inference, this suggestion addresses itself to the second question as well as the third, and brings up—or perhaps rightly concludes from—a discussion of the role, the very existence, of the predominantly Negro medical school.

Ultimately, there should be no predominantly Negro anything, unless of their own choice Negroes would like whatever it might be. Surely the ultimate aim of all programs to aid underprivileged groups is to do away with the need for programs. The sentiment of the Macy Conference was clearly against the establishment of additional Negro medical schools. But the discontinuance of Howard and Meharry was deemed out of the question. Their roles should be reviewed as time goes on. But their programs should be strengthened and their existence, for many reasons, unchallenged.

First, at a time when more medical schools are critically needed, existing ones cannot be destroyed.

Second, Meharry Medical School feels that its special need for existence is its empathy for the disadvantaged. It serves as role model and inspiration. More important, its partnership with the community, one of interdependence, makes it an important center of health care, education, and research. It provides community leadership, guidance, and support. Meharry's Department of Pediatrics received a grant from the Children's Bureau in order to establish a health care center for children in the college vicinity. Meharry is particularly interested in neighborhood health teams of medical and supportive personnel working together. It is interested—perhaps more open-mindedly so than some of its white counterparts—in creating career ladders that begin with the very young and inspire them to a variety of health careers.

Third, for however long there continue to be pressures upon Negro students *because they are Negro,* it is possible that some of them will prefer to go to Negro medical schools.

The individual student who finds himself the only Negro, or one of two or three Negroes, in a medical school class, may find that the pressures of that very fact interfere with his performance. Granted, this is a highly individual matter: some people are far more sensitive to such (or to any) pressures than others are. Some people are pressured more than other people, too. Just the "We're counting on you" letter from home is pressure. The feeling every time you get up to answer a question in a crowded lecture hall that you are answering for all Negroes is a pressure. The problem of finding someone to take out on a date is a pressure. Again, not all Negroes feel this, but surely those who do cannot be criticized for choosing to study in a school where they will not experience what for them is a pressure.

Some Negroes have gone through their lower education, including college, in "integrated" (for which read "predominantly white") schools. They may have felt it necessary, in that context, to participate to the fullest in the life of the institution—in sports, in student government, in other extracurricular activities, in politics—and they may not want to feel pressured from within to perpetuate this need in medical school.

These were some of the reasons reported by participants in the conference. They were not shared by all, but they were considered highly worthy of respect. Some participants reported on the confidences of Negro students who felt that they were accepted in predominantly white medical schools "up to a point." There seemed often to be a point where acceptance stopped. Sometimes it was sharing lecture notes or bull sessions; sometimes condescension on the part of faculty members who answered not the question you were asking but another and a much more elementary question. Sometimes the limit of acceptance became evident with the decisions about which students were to be sent to which hospitals as part of their clerkships.

49

Reactions and reaction times differ. A great deal depends, for the individual, on his ability to cope with such pressures, assuming he wants to cope—to have to cope—at all.

To sum up, the members of the conference felt that the two existing Negro medical schools should continue to exist as such as long as the social pressures which brought them into being continue. Probably these schools afford opportunities for medical education of Negroes who otherwise would not have entrée into medicine. There is, it must be said, some ambivalence about Howard and Meharry and even some difference of opinion about whether or not Meharry can fill this special role. However, the role will change as society changes. The schools will be needed, in their changed form, because they are medical schools, long after they may cease to be Negro medical schools. Every effort should be made to strengthen their programs.

The special problems of the Negro student who does move from the campus of a predominantly Negro college to a medical school in which practically all of the other students and the faculty are white, or even the Negro student who has gone to integrated schools and finds himself in a minority of one or two or ten in medical school, must be recognized and dealt with. He should receive all possible support from the administration, the faculty, and especially his classmates. Again, this support must be given with true humaneness. The student will not want to be singled out; the support should be there, but it may have to be subtle.

Not only the Negro medical schools, but all medical schools should establish special programs to salvage able Negro applicants who are not fully qualified for the study of medicine. These special programs have many variants. Students might be sent to liberal arts colleges to fulfill their academic requirements. They should be assured by the medical school to which they had applied when they transfer to these undergraduate colleges that they will be given continued support on the path to and through medical school.

Proposals for such programs are based in part on the assumption that Negro applicants who are rejected by medical schools because of grades and medical admissions tests have an undetermined but perhaps greater potential than other rejectees with similar grades and scores. The assumption is based largely on the verbal handicap from which many Negro applicants suffer and which affects their performance on admissions tests. The charge is made that the MCAT is culture-linked: that is, its frame of reference is the white middle-class experience and not the American Negro experience. Exposure in a predominantly white college to supplementary English courses, or to other courses in which the Negro student may be weak, may not only strengthen the student in the skill or subject in which he is deficient but may also fill in for him some of the culture gaps with which he has grown up. Regardless of race, the pool of rejected applicants contains many people who could do well in medical school and who could become effective physicians if they were given a chance.

For students considered intellectually competent but in need of additional experience before matriculation into medical school, elastic preclinical programs might be established. Such programs, which might take two years or three, plus a summer or summers, would include the equivalent of the first two years of medical studies enriched with appropriate science and non-science courses. Students completing the program would embark upon their clinical studies in any of a number of four-year medical schools. Indeed, a pool of such students already exists. These students might be readied to fill vacancies which occur in the second or third year of medical school as a result of the high attrition rate.

As a variant of this proposal, special two-year medical schools might be established in association with Negro colleges or state universities—bringing together strong predominantly Negro state universities or colleges with one or more strong medical schools. The staffs from the medical schools would teach in these schools and the students who qualified by going to them could then be brought into the medical schools at the third-year level.

The possibility of a multiple-track system within such programs, leading to careers in allied health professions, was discussed in this context. The subject of multiple-track systems of medical education or, more particularly, multiple-track health services was seen by some of the participants as a class issue rather than a race issue. Discussion of them seems to belong with the long-range rather than the immediate programs or proposals. But two-year medical schools might be established in the immediate future, if the roadblocks of convention and class pressures can be broken through. That would be a start.

As another variant in medical education, the four-year medical schools might institute one year of elective courses, so that a significant portion of the four-year program would meet the special needs or special talents of individual students. This loosening up of the curriculum, which has already been effected in some of the medical schools, such as Duke, will allow for more elective time—presumably of special use to students who have weaknesses arising from their earlier education.

For Negro students who show promise for medicine, additional programs should be established along the lines of existing special programs to strengthen education at the college level. These programs might be modeled after the Haverford Post-Baccalaureate year or the Harvard-Yale-Columbia Intensive Summer Program or might well combine the two, with intensive summer work before the junior and senior years (either or both) and then another summer and a full academic year after graduation. There are any number of possible variants.

The Emory Law School summer program in torts can also serve as a model. Such special summer programs might allow students to test their ability in a single course such as anatomy and at the same time gain some sense of security in the environment of a medical school.

Programs should be flexible enough to allow for individual needs and differences. Academic work should surely be combined with counseling and follow-up recommendations to medical schools. Economic assistance must be available as needed. Dedicated men and women to administer the program must be found. Students must be sought out and encouraged to participate. Subtle forms of discrimination must be recognized and offset. The problem is one of overcoming or compensating not merely for weak college education, but for an entire system of poor education. What Haverford and its associated colleges have done, other schools can do and must do.

The question of special programs for Negro women for medicine was variously interpreted, an indication of its complexity. The fact behind the question has already been cited: although there are more female than male Negro college students, there are more male than female Negro medical students and physicians. Women Negro college students do not aspire in large numbers (or proportions) to become physicians. Part of the reason is economic—the matriarchy which was a heritage of slavery and its aftermath lingers: Negro women still have familial economic burdens which prevent many of them from going to graduate or professional school.

But beyond this area of fact there are questions. Is the Negro woman discriminated against in medical education because she is a Negro or because she is a woman? Should there be special educational *and professional* concessions, as there are in some other countries, to women because they are mothers? Should Negro women in fact step aside—will they be indeed only too happy to do so—as Negro men are given more opportunities for economic, social, and professional status? Is it true or is it a shibboleth that Negro women have something special to contribute to medicine because of their history or simply because they are women?

The question *should there be special programs to attract Negro women to medicine* was answered with a *yes* by some of the participants. They felt that there should be special arrangements for women in the medical profession. They should have several years maternity leave for each child; they should have school vacations off; time should be arranged for them to be with their children when they are ill. This plan did not find favor with all the participants, some of whom felt that women must be prepared to pull their own weight, assume equal professional responsibility with men.

Others felt that this was not the point at all, but rather that the key word in the question was "attract," and that Negro women, who do have a special contribution to make to medicine, should be given special educational and financial opportunities to go to medical school and that the rigidity of internships and residencies should be loosened up. These suggestions did not, however, lay to rest the question that Negro women might then be competing for medical school admission with Negro men. The ultimate answer to that question is probably that when all prejudices are put aside, sex as well as race or class, the best man or woman will win. Until then, and with the ever-present need for more physicians uppermost, the sentiment of the majority seemed to be that in the short-range view Negro women already in college in larger numbers than Negro men should not be discriminated against by the medical schools or by premedical advisers because they are women, but rather should be encouraged and given financial support to enable them to study medicine.

No specific proposals were made on the ninth question: Are there problems at the internship and residency level? To oversimplify, yes. The Charles Drew Memorial Hospital and Medical School plan described in Chapter Two was begun as a consequence of and a partial solution to those problems. But the question led to a long series of additional questions—searching, nagging questions for which no immediate answers were available at the Conference. These questions, even without answers, are worth recording here, but they belong with the next chapter—the one on long-range plans and proposals.

IV

WHAT CAN BE DONE: LONG RANGE

Not only the physician but the profession, not only the Negro but the nation, stands at a point in history from which perspectives on the future seem to break down neatly into short-range and long. Again and again at the conference this dichotomy, if indeed it is one, was used. There are some steps, however, which can and must be taken to effect immediate change. Other steps must be taken to insure that change will be long-lasting and accelerative.

Attacks upon a problem short-range—within five years—call for "measures." For the long range, however, we look for solutions. The "measures" may be avowedly stopgap or crash measures which are intended as much to demonstrate our belief in progress as to be actual examples of progress. They may be segments or samples of the solutions which are large-scale and long-range. They inevitably concern themselves with individuals rather than with large groups. No one could in good faith say that to find places for 100 or even 1,000 Negro medical students in the next five years is *a* solution, much less *the* solution to this problem, or that giving financial aid to five predominantly Negro colleges is a (or the) solution.

Long-range solutions are inseparable from the vast social issues of which the problem of Negroes for medicine is a mere symptom.

The problem of getting more Negroes into the medical profession cannot, in the long run, be separated from the problem of educating more Negroes and educating them well. We are talking not only about improving curriculum, faculty, and facilities at *all* Negro colleges (though that is itself a complicated and expensive job), but about improving education and educational systems in the high schools and elementary schools attended by Negroes all over the country and about early identification, guidance, and support of both the potentially gifted and the less gifted who have good potential. To enable those interested in going to medical school to go if they qualify, and to open up other professional and intellectual highways to them, we must get more Negroes into college. This involves motivation (which in turn means realistic promise of rewards) as well as education.

To attain this goal will require enormous expenditures. It calls for great flexibility, for the same plans and curricula will not work in rural as in urban areas, in the North as in the South, with one student as with another. We have to be prepared to fail and to start again.

The cities, where much of the problem is centered, have not yet found a really satisfactory solution. New York, for example, has tried weeding out the "troublemakers" (though it has not yet weeded out the trouble), putting them in classes of seven or fewer with two or more teachers, using one teacher per 20 for the remaining students, and starting schooling very early. The city has done this, at least, on paper; in the school it is not always so neat. And the city has reported both some success and some discouragement. It has tried—or is trying—to pump in all manner of "special services" with euphemistic names to go with them: cluster teachers, opportunity classes, enrichment programs, junior guidance classes, halfway classes, Head Start, and "600" schools. Again reports of the results conflict, to the frustration of all involved.

New methods of teaching must also be developed, methods of teaching reading and the other uses of language particularly. In the North, the problem of the middle-class white teacher teaching the lower-class Negro child, whose feelings and pressures the teacher can only dimly comprehend, must be overcome. In the South, teaching must be made more attractive and rewarding. Curricula must be revamped in various ways. It must be made economically possible as well as socially realistic for children to stay in school.

But we are talking now about long-range solutions to a social ill so overwhelming that one almost cannot take in all of it. It is much too soon to know whether or not these experiments, and many, many others like and unlike them, are going to fail or succeed. (We must also work out, with the benefit of the best minds we have, what we mean by "succeed" and what we mean by "fail." Surely we do not mean simply good or bad education.) Educational programs, however vast and competent, can succeed fully only when other social measures do: only when attitudes are changed.

These are not original ideas, being said here for the first time, but they need saying at every opportunity, to every willing and recalcitrant ear.

Long-range solutions to the problem of Negroes for medicine include improvement of the status and opportunities for service of Negroes in the allied health professions. The nation, and the medical profession, are going to have to turn more and more to the paramedical or allied health professions for help. A competent technician can help a physician extend the range and extent of medical services to people who need medical care. The services of such paramedical personnel—including nurses, laboratory technicians, and x-ray technicians, for example—are increasingly important in the practice of medicine. The unfilled demand for such personnel remains high and offers opportunities now for people interested in medical careers but who, for any reason, fail to become physicians.

The position of professional Negro women vis-à-vis Negro men will change eventually, and the number of Negro women in medicine *may decrease*. Admissions policies and opportunities offered should reflect enlightenment about this volatile and complicated subject. Hopefully, this problem, along with many others, will disappear rather than be solved when the color of a man's skin is no longer a matter of concern or even of interest.

Long-range solutions must deal with the problems of the Negro intern, resident, and practicing physician. Existing ills must be exposed and cured. If the situation has improved in the past dozen years, and there is reason to believe that it has, this should be publicized so that Negroes aspiring to medical careers may learn what their opportunities are. Only then will the long-range incentives we have referred to become known and real so that Negro college and medical school graduates can feel free to continue their training and specialization and join fully in the profession, with equal hope and equal opportunity for advancement.

Is the current Negro medical school graduate getting into the mainstream of American medicine? To answer that question and to act upon the answer, if action is needed, leads to a great many other questions.

Are there still in this country institutions which methodically exclude Negroes from their programs? Do the superior teaching hospitals, hiding behind the seeming fairness of the National Interne Matching Program, effectively discriminate against Negroes? (Of course, this question can be asked the other way round: do superior medical-school graduates systematically discriminate against some hospitals?) The ultimate question becomes what can be done about these discriminatory practices if they do exist.

Residency selection is highly variable. On what bases are decisions made? Are there any Negro interns who are systematically being excluded from the better residency training programs because of their race? Are there interns who do a satisfactory or even superior job but are not selected as residents?

Are there quota systems within either the internship or the residency programs?

Are there significant differences between the internship-residency selections of Negro graduates from Meharry and Howard and the selections made of Negro graduates from the predominantly white medical schools?

What per cent of Negro graduates are taking straight internships, mixed internships, and rotating internships?

Is there any significant relationship between the internship-residency selection and the stipend paid? If so, what can be done about it?

What per cent of Negro graduates are selecting internships in university-affiliated hospitals as opposed to non-university-affiliated hospitals, and what per cent are accepting Veterans Administration, US Public Health, and military internships? Is there a significant deviation from the national average? Should this group be studied?

What per cent of Negro graduates must discontinue their training after their internships or shorten training while in the middle of their residencies to go into medical practice for financial reasons? If the per cent is significant, these people need help.

Are there comparatively more or fewer Negro physicians in the specialties now than there were ten years ago? Which specialties are overloaded and where are the needs greatest? Are there trends of exclusion in specific specialties and sub-specialties?

Is the feeling pervasive that Negroes are incapable of basic scientific research? What are the consequences of such a feeling, if it exists, and what can be done about it? Is the impression that some Negroes have that this feeling exists among medical educators based on a Negro hypersensitivity rather than fact?

After they have graduated from medical school, is relatively less attention paid to Negroes in the middle and lower thirds of their classes than to white medical graduates in the comparable positions?

Are the best Negro graduates being encouraged toward academic careers, or are they shunted away from any academic ambitions they may have?

What can be done about inbreeding in the Negro medical schools?

About the frustrations of Negro doctors in urban areas?

About the fact that many Negro doctors are not joining the American Medical Association?

About referrals? Affiliations?

About Negro hospitals as deterrents to professional integration?

About involvement of successful Negro physicians in the struggle for integration of Negro physicians?

About the exercise of pressure by power groups in the community? the nation?

Answers must be given to these questions. Solutions must be found. In the long-range perspective, it is not nearly enough to educate people for jobs which are then frustrating, discriminatory, second-rate, dead-end, or unobtainable. It is not enough to train a handful of Negro physicians. It is not enough to provide adequate medical care to a handful of Negroes.

Until there is good medical care for all, until there is opportunity for all to develop to their utmost potential, until every man is allowed to contribute to the common good, we shall not have done enough.

AFTERWORD

To end this book on any note other than humility would be presumptuous and pietistic. The "problem"—the term itself an ironic understatement—the position of the Negro in American society and in the society of man, does not reduce itself to, nor can it be resolved by, the position of the Negro in medicine. The enormity of the issue struck the writer in seeing how long it took just to prepare this book: one endeavor within one profession to *approach* the task before us in this century.

This book can hope to bring into being some improvement in education, in guidance, in economic power for the prospective or potential Negro physician. It can contribute to the exposure of existing conflicts, tensions, injustices. That is all it can hope to do. It cannot *be* a solution. The problem would not be solved if every proposal in this book were acted upon, as some are already being and others surely will be.

Again, help from the foundations, pilot projects, and other forms of attention to individuals can set the stage, but they can never be enough. Help is needed on a massive scale. The war against ignorance, against inferior education, against inequity of educational opportunity—against inequity—requires an all-out effort.

As others have pointed out, the time is no more when we can allow ourselves the luxury of blame, or even of guilt. The present is a product of the past, but it is not altogether a product of will. And the future cannot be made better merely by assigning responsibility. Change must come from all corners; it must involve everyone—not only the rural farm boy, white as well as black, but the successful physician, black as well as white.

This means federal financial support to educate every Negro to the limit of his individual capacity. It means vast social, cultural, and economic programs. The foundations can launch programs to point the way, in anticipation of the end of the war in Vietnam. When that war ends, this is the front we must fight on.

We end where we began. The position of the Negro in medicine is but a part, a measure, a reflection of the position of the Negro. That does not begin in medical school, in college, in high school, in elementary school, in the home, *in utero*. It begins in an underground moat in Nigeria and in the minds of men. For it to change will require the purification of many suns.

LIST OF PARTICIPANTS

Macy Conference on Negroes for Medicine, June 25–28, 1967, held in cooperation with the National Medical Fellowships, Inc.

ANDERSON, Robert S., M.D.
Chairman, Interim Committee
Meharry Medical College

BARBER, James D., Ph.D.
Director of Graduate Studies
Department of Political Science
Yale University

BECKER, E. Lovell, M.D.
Department of Medicine
The New York Hospital-Cornell
    Medical Center

BERRY, George Packer, M.D.
Dean Emeritus
Harvard Medical School

BERRYHILL, W. Reece, M.D.
Director, Division of Education
    and Research in Community
    Medical Care
The University of North Carolina
    at Chapel Hill

BOWERS, John Z., M.D.
President
Josiah Macy, Jr. Foundation

BRANSON, Herman, Ph.D.
Head, Department of Physics
Howard University

CADBURY, William E., Jr., Ph.D.
Director, Post-Baccalaureate Fel-
    lowship Program
Haverford College

CEITHAML, Joseph, Ph.D.
Dean of Students
The University of Chicago
    School of Medicine

COMER, James P., M.D.
Child Study Center
Yale University

CURTIS, James L., M.D.
Psychiatrist

DENT, Albert W., LL.D.
President
Dillard University

FAULKNER, James M., M.D.
National Fund for Medical Edu-
    cation

FAWCETT, Don W., M.D.
Hersey Professor of Anatomy
Harvard Medical School

GODWIN, Winfred, Ph.D.
Director
Southern Regional Educational
    Board

GRAEF, Irving, M.D.
Member, Board of Directors
National Medical Fellowships, Inc.

HARDEN, K. Albert, M.D.
Dean
College of Medicine
Howard University

HEARD, Alexander, Ph.D.
Chancellor
Vanderbilt University

HOLLAND, Bernard, M.D.
Chairman, Department of Psychiatry
Emory University
School of Medicine

HUBBARD, W.M., Jr., M.D.
Dean
The University of Michigan
Medical School

HUSSEY, Hugh H., M.D.
Director, Division of Scientific Activities
American Medical Association

JOHNSON, Samuel
Education Counseling Service
United Presbyterian Church in U.S.A.

KENNEDY, William B., M.D.
Associate Dean
University of Pennsylvania
The School of Medicine

LOGAN, Myra, M.D., F.A.C.S.
Upper Manhattan Medical Group

LUCKEY, E. Hugh, M.D.
President
The New York Hospital-Cornell
Medical Center

MacLEOD, Colin M., M.D.
Vice President for Medical Affairs
The Commonwealth Fund

McBAY, Henry C., Ph.D.
Chairman, Department of Chemistry
Morehouse College

McKITTRICK, Leland S., M.D.
Honorary Surgeon
The Massachusetts General Hospital

McLEAN, Franklin C., M.D.
Secretary and Treasurer
National Medical Fellowships, Inc.

MELLINKOFF, Sherman M., M.D.
Dean
School of Medicine
University of California, Los Angeles

ORGAN, Claude H., Jr., M.D., F.A.C.S.
Assistant Clinical Professor of Surgery
The Creighton University

REITZES, Mrs. Hilde
Executive Secretary
National Medical Fellowship, Inc.

ROBERTSON, Alexander, M.D.
Executive Director
Milbank Memorial Fund

ROGERS, David E., M.D.
Chairman, Department of Medicine
Vanderbilt University
School of Medicine

ROSENHAUPT, Hans, Ph.D.
National Director
Woodrow Wilson National
  Fellowship Foundation

SEVERINGHAUS, Aura E., Ph.D.
Director, Macy Foundation Program
Preparation for Medical Education
  in the Traditionally Negro College

SILVER, George A., M.D.
Deputy Assistant Secretary for
  Health and Scientific Affairs
Department of Health, Education,
  and Welfare

SPURLOCK, Jeanne, M.D.
Chief of Child Psychiatry
Michael Reese Hospital

WATSON, Robert B., M.D.
School of Public Health
University of North Carolina at
  Chapel Hill

WOODWARD, Celeste L., M.D.
Physician

WOODWARD, Theodore E.,
  M.D.
Chairman, Department of Medicine
University of Maryland
School of Medicine

ZURCHER, Arnold J., Ph.D.
Executive Director
Alfred P. Sloan Foundation

SELECTED BIBLIOGRAPHY

Note: Although this book was based essentially on the Proceedings of the Macy Conference on Negroes for Medicine, occasionally it was necessary to elaborate on or clarify a point which had been made. Sometimes this was done by phone or by correspondence, sometimes by reference to printed sources. The following bibliography, then, is highly selected.

A Better Chance, *Newsletter*, 376 Boylston Street, Boston, Massachusetts.

Datagrams, Educational Research Service, Vol. 8, No. 8, February 1967.
Educational Talent Section: Report No. 1, Bureau of Higher Education; Office of Education; Department of Health, Education, and Welfare, May 19, 1967, 16 pp.

Educational Talent Section: Report No. 2, Bureau of Higher Education; Office of Education; Department of Health, Education, and Welfare, June 1, 1967, 7 pp.

Educational Talent Section. Report No. 3, Bureau of Higher Education; Office of Education; Department of Health, Education, and Welfare, June 26, 1967, 3 pp.

Fichter, Joseph H., *Graduates of Predominantly Negro Colleges,* Class of 1964, The National Institutes of Health, with joint sponsorship by the U.S. Department of Labor and National Science Foundation, Public Health Service Publication No. 1571, Government Printing Office, Washington, D.C., 1967, xix, 262 pp.

Flake, Tom, "Meharry Is Convinced It Is Needed," *Southern Education Report*, November 1967, pp. 10–11.

Harvard-Yale-Columbia Intensive Summer Studies Program, Report of the Administrative Committee, 1967. Unpublished manuscript.

Idea Exchange, Vol. 3, No. 2, December 1967, 29 pp. Published by Educational Associates, Inc. for Upward Bound. Washington, D.C.

Institutions of Higher Education Receiving Grants Under Title III, The Higher Education Act of 1965, Fiscal Year 1967.

Johansen, Gary, "Science on Saturdays," Sunday World-Herald Magazine of the Midlands, *Omaha World-Herald*, June 4, 1967, pp. 19–20.

Manual for the Preparation of Title III Proposals, Office of Education, U.S. Department of Health, Education, and Welfare; Fiscal Year 1969, iii, 24 pp. (1968)

McGrath, Earl J., *The Predominantly Negro Colleges and Universities in Transition*, A Publication of the Institute of Higher Education, New York: Teachers College, Columbia University, 1965, xv, 204 pp.

National Medical Fellowships Newsletter, Chicago, January 1967, 8 pp.

The Negro and Higher Education in the South, A Statement by the Commission on Higher Educational Opportunity in the South, Southern Regional Education Board, Atlanta, Georgia, 1967, vii, 44 pp.

New Opportunities for Negroes in Medicine, Chicago: National Medical Fellowships, Inc., 1965, 36 pp.

Proceedings, Josiah Macy, Jr. Foundation Conference on Negroes for Medicine, Fort Lauderdale, Florida, June 25 to 28, 1967. Unpublished, 666 manuscript pp.

Proceedings, Josiah Macy, Jr. Foundation on Preparation for Medical Education in the Traditionally Negro College, Atlanta, Georgia, February 25 to 27, 1968. Unpublished, 576 manuscript pp.

Public Law 89–329, November 8, 1965, Government Printing Office, Washington, D.C., 52 pp.

Public Law 89–752, November 3, 1966, Government Printing Office, Washington, D.C., 6 pp.

Reitzes, Dietrich C., *Negroes and Medicine,* for The Commonwealth Fund, Cambridge: Harvard University Press, 1958, xxiv, 40 p. Introduction by Franklin C. McLean.

Reitzes, Hilde, "Draft Paper on the History of the National Medical Fellowships, Inc.," June 1967. Unpublished, 12 manuscript pp.

Severinghaus, Aura E., Harry J. Carman, and William E. Cadbury, Jr., *Preparation for Medical Education: A Restudy*, The Report of the Committee on the Resurvey of Preprofessional Education in the Liberal Arts College, Association of American Medical Colleges, New York, Toronto, London. The Blakiston Division, McGraw-Hill Book Company, Inc., 1953 and 1961, xxvi, 404 pp.

Sugg, Redding S., Jr., *SREB: A Current Appraisal*, Southern Regional Education Board, Atlanta, Georgia, 1963, 87 pp.

Sugg, Redding S., Jr. and George Hilton Jones, *The Southern Regional Education Board*: Ten Years of Regional Cooperation in Higher Education, Baton Rouge: Louisiana State University Press, 1960, xv, 179 pp.

THE JOHNS HOPKINS PRESS

Designed by Arlene J. Sheer

Composed in Baskerville and Baskerville Display types
by Monotype Composition Company, Inc.

Printed offset by Universal Lithographers, Inc.
on 60 lb. Perkins and Squier R.

Bound by L.H. Jenkins, Inc. in Columbia Fictionette